Air, Air
All Around

For Caitlin and Molly—J.B.
For Elise and Pete—H.P.

Produced by Daniel Weiss Associates, Inc.
33 West 17 Street, New York, NY 10011
Copyright © 1990 Daniel Weiss Associates, Inc.,
and Al Jarnow.

Illustration copyright © 1990 Heidi Petach

Published by Silver Press, a division of
Silver Burdett Press, Inc., Simon & Schuster, Inc.
Prentice Hall Bldg., Englewood Cliffs, NJ 07632
For information address: Silver Press.

Printed in the United States of America
10 9 8 7 6 5 4 3 2 1

Library of Congress Cataloging-in-Publication Data

Barkan, Joanne.
Air, air around / written by Joanne Barkan; illustrated
by Heidi Petach.
p.   cm.—(First facts)
Summary: Describes, in simple text, the properties and uses of air,
where air is found, and why it's essential to life.
1. Air—Juvenile literature.   [1. Air.]   I. Petach, Heidi, ill.
II. Title.   III. Series: First facts
(Englewood Cliffs, N.J.)
QC161.2.B37 1989   89-39209
551.5—dc20   CIP
*   AC*
ISBN 0-671-68659-3   ISBN 0-671-68655-0 (lib. bdg.)

First Facts™

Air, Air All Around

Written by Joanne Barkan
Illustrated by Heidi Petach

Silver Press

Can you answer this riddle?
You swallow it, but you can't taste it.

You sniff it, but you can't smell it.

You watch it, but you can't see it.
What is it?

The answer is air!
Air is all around you.
Without air, no people, plants ,
or animals could live on Earth.

So how do you know that air is really there?

Blow up a balloon.
What makes it get bigger? Air does.

Push an upside-down glass into the bathtub water.
The air inside the glass makes it pop right up.

Blow through a straw into a glass of water.
What makes the water bubble?
That's right, air does.

Let a piece of paper fall to the floor.
Swish! It floats on air as it drops.

Air is made of many invisible gases.
A gas has no shape of its own.
It will spread out and fill whatever it is in.

Air will fill something as tiny as a bubble or as big as a circus tent!

Without air, you wouldn't be able
to hear anything.
Air carries sound from one place to another.
Air carries the sound of a beating drum to your ears.

It carries the meows of the cat,

the music of the ice-cream truck,

and the laughter of all your friends.

Do you believe the air around you is filled
with thousands of floating specks?
It's true!
Shine a flashlight in a dark room.
Now look into the beam of light.
You'll see thousands of specks of dust swirling.

Even clean air has specks floating in it.
Besides dust, there's salt from the ocean,
and living things that are too tiny to see.

Smoke from furnaces, fumes from cars and buses,
and dangerous gases from factories
also float in the air.
They can be harmful to your health.
Air that's dirty is called polluted air.

Here is some good news:
Today many cities and towns
are trying to clean up their air.

People need clean air to breathe.
Animals and plants need clean air, too.
When you breathe in, your body takes in oxygen.
Oxygen is one of the gases in the air.
Oxygen lets you turn the food you eat
into energy for running, jumping, and playing.

When you breathe out,
you breathe out a gas called carbon dioxide.
Plants take in carbon dioxide to make food.
Guess what plants give off.
They give off oxygen for you to breathe.

You've just taken another breath.
The oxygen you've breathed in
has gone into your lungs.

Now it's entering your blood.
Your blood will carry that oxygen
to every part of your body—
even to the tips of your toes!

Air does not seem heavy,
but it does weigh something.
This weight is called air pressure.
It presses around everything in the world.
It's pressing around you right now!

Don't worry. You can't feel it because the air
inside your body is pressing out at the same time.

A lot of air can be squeezed into a small place.
You can pump air into beach balls,
air mattresses, and tires until they get hard.

With enough air inside, your bike tires
will hold up your bike *and* you.

Airplanes use air pressure to fly.
Their wings are shaped so the air pressure
under the plane helps to hold it up.
Helicopters and gliders use air pressure to fly, too.

So do cardinals and dragonflies,
and all other flying creatures in the world.

Birds and insects also use the wind
to stay up in the air.

Wind is air moving across the Earth.
Sometimes it moves as a gentle breeze.

Sometimes the wind blows harder—
so hold onto your hat!

Wind can be dangerous when it's part of a storm.
A hurricane starts over the ocean.
Its winds send huge waves crashing onto the beach.

A tornado starts on land.
Its spinning winds can lift a car.

The air outside is part of what
makes up the weather.
When the air is cold—br-r-r!—bundle up.

When the air is very warm,
it's time for a swim.

Clouds are tiny drops of water
that gather high up in the air.
When the drops of water get big enough,
they fall through the air as rain.

If the air is cold, they might come down
as snowflakes or icy hail.

Air surrounds the Earth like a thick blanket.
This blanket of air is called the atmosphere.

At night, the atmosphere holds in heat
and keeps the Earth from getting too cold.

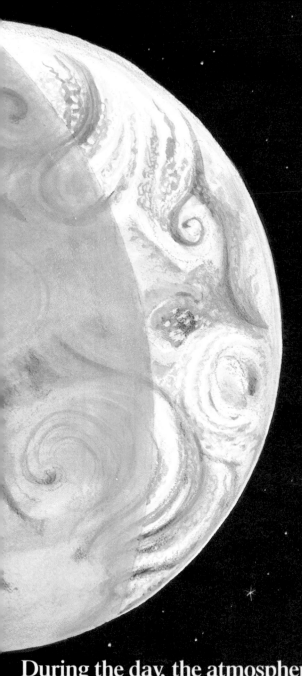

During the day, the atmosphere acts like a huge
umbrella and keeps the sun from burning the Earth.

The higher up you go, the less oxygen
there is in the atmosphere.
If you climb a very tall mountain,
you'll have to carry oxygen in a
tank to help you breathe.

Much higher up, there's no air.
That's why astronauts in space
wear oxygen tanks.

Down on Earth, you can play outside.
You can watch the birds fly through the air.
Or you can see the wind lift the kites
and whisk sailboats across the pond.
It's a fine day.
So take a deep breath of air!